Hayden-Reece Learns What To Do if Children See Private Pictures or Private Movies

or

Private Movies

by Holly-ann Martin

Hayden-Reece Learns What To Do if Children See Private Pictures or Private Movies
by Holly-ann Martin

Published September 2016
by Safe 4 Kids (Aust) Pty Ltd
www.safe4kids.com.au
PO Box 367
Armadale WA 6992
Australia
©2016 Safe4Kids

Illustrations by Marilyn Fahie
Cover designed by Steve Horton

Printed in China
Hung Hing Offset Printing Co Ltd

National Library of Australia Cataloguing-in-Publication entry
Creator: Martin, Holly-ann, author.

Title: Hayden-Reece learns what to do if children see private
  pictures or private movies / Holly-ann Martin ; Marilyn Fahie ;
  Steve Horton .

ISBN: 9780980529487 (hardback)

Subjects: Children and pornography.
  Child welfare.
  Pornography--Social aspects.

Other Creators/Contributors:
  Fahie, Marilyn, illustrator.
  Horton, Steve, book designer.

Dewey Number: 649.7

To my beautiful Great Nieces:

Shaylah, Blysse, Isabella,Darcey, Imogen, Evelyn and Imarlia.

May you all grow up in a world where children feel safe.

Note to Parents, Carers and Teachers

I have written this book to help parents, carers and teachers discuss with children the negative impact pornography may have on them, and to teach children what to do if they see pornographic images. This book is designed for adults to read to children to educate them.

It is advisable you read this book first, to familiarise yourself with the content and prepare for any discussions that may come up with your children. Use the parents', carers' and teachers' information section and discussion questions at the back of this book, to help generate conversations on the negative effects of pornography.

Hayden-Reece Learns What To Do if Children See Private Pictures or Private Movies is the third in a series of educational children's books on child-abuse-prevention education (protective behaviours).

The first book in this series – *Matilda Learns a Valuable Lesson*, looks at unwanted touching (nonsexual) and teaches children if they feel unsafe they need to seek help from an adult they trust (a member of their Safety Team or Safety Network). If one adult doesn't listen, then they need to persist and tell another adult they trust and to keep telling until an adult helps them, and they feel safe again.

The second book in this series – *Hayden-Reece Learns a Valuable Lesson That Private Means Just for You*, examines the concept of public and private. The book teaches children the difference between public and private, and discusses public and private rooms, body functions, clothing, behaviours and language, and culminates in teaching children the correct anatomical names for their private body parts. It is very important children are able to use the correct names for their private body parts in case they need to disclose they have suffered some form of abuse.

Hayden-Reece Learns What To Do if Children See Private Pictures or Private Movies follows on from *Hayden-Reece Learns a Valuable Lesson That Private Means Just for You*. It revises the concept of public and private and then leads into the discussion on pornography. In this book I call pornography 'private pictures' and 'private movies'. This helps reinforce the concept of public and private with the children.

I hope you and your children enjoy this book.

Holly-ann Martin

Yesterday Miss Martin taught her class the difference between public and private. She told the children that public means there are other people around and private means 'just for you'.

Before Miss Martin started the public and private lesson, she told the children there were some rules they needed to follow, because they would be using some private words that they would not normally say at school. She explained that she didn't want to hear

these words out in the playground or other places around the school, because school is a public place. These words were only to be discussed in this classroom, at this time. Miss Martin also asked the class to try and not giggle, explaining that people giggle when talking about private things because they are embarrassed, but that each student needed to know about this subject and she thought they were grown-up enough to talk about it without any laughing or silliness.

If they didn't feel they could stick to the rules they could go to a buddy class. All the class agreed to the rules; no one wanted to go to buddy class and miss out on the lesson. The children learnt about public and private rooms, body functions and behaviours, and that some things, like burping, nose picking and farting, are done in private. No one wants to see or hear those private things. They also learnt that some clothes are private too.

The children learnt the correct names for their private body parts: boys have a mouth, a bottom, a penis and testicles; girls have a mouth, a bottom, breasts, a vulva and a vagina.

Miss Martin decided that in today's lesson they would talk about something else that is private.

Miss Martin pulled out her mobile phone and asked the class if they would like to see some pictures and a movie of her holiday? The children were all excited to see the pictures, because they knew Miss Martin had just returned from a trip to Africa where she had gone cage-diving with great white sharks.

After showing the children her photos, Miss Martin asked the class if it was okay for them to see these pictures. The children all agreed it was. Then Miss Martin explained that there are other kinds of pictures and movies which are not okay for children to see.

These are called private pictures or private movies, which show private adult activities. In these pictures and movies people may have no clothes on and you can see their private body parts. Sometimes in these private pictures and movies people are being very cruel and hurting other people, which is not okay!

Miss Martin explained to the children that it wasn't healthy for children's brains to see private pictures or movies, and that seeing them might give them nightmares. Sometimes you can't stop thinking about what you have seen, which can be confusing or upsetting.

Miss Martin asked the class where children might see private pictures or movies.

"On computers," said Lauren.

"On phones," said Jeremy.

"How about TV?" asked David.

"On tablets," said Karen.

"Video games," suggested Brendon.

Hayden-Reece asked,

"What about tattoos?"

"Yes, even tattoos,"

agreed Miss Martin.

"Now, class," said Miss Martin, "What would you do if you were using one of the school's iPads and you typed in 'Fairies', and a picture came up on the screen of a lady with no clothes on, wearing a pair of big fairy wings? What would you do?"

"Turn it off," said Elliot.

"Close my eyes," suggested Mary.

"Show the other kids," said Hayden-Reece. Miss Martin smiled. "Thank you for being honest, Hayden-Reece, but you must not show other children those kinds of pictures. That would be breaking the law. You need to be over 18 years of age to see pictures like that."

"Tell a grown-up," said Lauren.

"Good thinking, Lauren!" replied Miss Martin.

Miss Martin explained, "What I want you to do is to turn off the iPad or computer, so other children can't see the pictures. Then I need you to tell your teacher. If it happens at home or out of school, you need to tell an adult you trust, hopefully someone who is on your Safety Team. Remember, a Safety Team is five trusted adults you can talk to about anything. They need to know what has happened so they can help you understand what you have seen."

"But won't we get into trouble?" asked Hayden-Reece.

"No," explained Miss Martin. "There are people out there who want to shock children by showing them private pictures. If anyone shows you private pictures – whether they are other children, teenagers or adults, and even adults in your family, or if you come across these pictures or movies by accident – you need to tell someone on your Safety Team. It's not your fault, and you won't get into trouble."

Then Miss Martin explained something very interesting. "Unfortunately these private pictures and private movies can affect some people's brains and the way they think. Even adults can be affected by these pictures and movies. "Sometimes when people see private pictures or private movies, they get excited about what they have seen, and they get hooked on that feeling and want to see more and more! But this is not good for our brains, particularly for children, because your brains are still developing and it can change the way you think. It can be confusing, you may feel you want to see more of these private pictures or private movies, but you know it is wrong, and these pictures and movies can give you nightmares. Sometimes you may find it hard to concentrate at school because of what you have seen. You could say private pictures and private movies are like poison to your brain.

"If you do see private pictures or private movies I need you to say out loud, 'That's private,' and turn away or close your eyes. I need you to turn off the iPad or computer and tell a trusted adult so they can help you understand what you have seen."

A few days later Hayden-Reece was on his iPad watching Minecraft videos. Suddenly, another video caught his eye, so he clicked on it. The video started to play; he saw naked adults in a lounge room.

He knew straight away that this was the kind

of movie Miss Martin had spoken about.

It made him feel uncomfortable;

he had his Early Warning Signs.

He said out loud, "That's private,"

and he hit the home button.

He remembered what Miss Martin had said,

"You must tell someone on your Safety Team."

But he wondered, would his mum tell him off? Would she take

his iPad away? What if his mum didn't know what Miss Martin

taught the class?

Hayden-Reece decided not to say anything.

He went to bed that night but couldn't get the movie out of his mind. He finally dropped off to sleep but woke up after having a bad dream about what he had seen.

In the morning after breakfast, Hayden-Reece went up to his mum when no one else was around and said, "Mum, can I tell you something?" His mum could tell that something was really worrying Hayden-Reece.

"You know you can tell me anything," she said.

They went out the back door and sat on the back steps. Hayden-Reece took a big breath and said, "Yesterday I was watching Minecraft videos and another video came up that looked interesting. The next thing I knew a movie started that had grown-ups with no clothes on and this lady was screaming! I didn't tell you straight away because I thought you would take away my iPad."

"How did it make you feel?" asked his mum.

"It made me feel uncomfortable. I feel confused because in a way it was also a nice feeling and exciting. I couldn't stop thinking about it, and it gave me a bad dream."

"This may sound a bit strange," said Hayden-Reece's mum, "but the feelings you have described to me are normal. You are still a child and you are not ready for what you saw. It can be very confusing for children and sometimes scary."

She gave him a hug.

"You didn't do anything wrong, and I'm glad you told me about it. Do you have any questions, or is there anything else worrying you?"

Hayden-Reece thought for a moment. "Is that what sex is?" he asked.

"The movie you saw showed people having sex, but what you saw is not how people should treat each other. You know that people should respect each other. The people in that movie are actors, not people who have chosen to be in a loving relationship with each other," said Mum. "It's normal to be curious about sex, and to find sexual pictures and videos exciting, but it can upset children to see pictures like that."

She gave him a big smile. "Remember, you can talk with me about anything. I am so proud that you told me about what you saw and how it made you feel."

That day at school Hayden-Reece told Miss Martin everything that had happened the night before.

"And you were right, Miss Martin!" he said. "Mum didn't tell me off or take away the iPad. She told me I could talk with her about anything, just like you told us."

Parents, Carers and Teachers Information

The ease with which pornography is accessible online is of great concern. Readily-available internet connections and mobile devices such as smart phones and tablets have changed our world and the way we communicate and source information. A downside of having the World Wide Web at our fingertips is the proliferation of free online pornography and the ease with which children can access it either knowingly or by accident.

There are many research papers and articles written by academics and medical practitioners on the potential harm pornography does to the developing brains of children. As parents, carers and teachers we try to protect children from online dangers including exposure to graphic, violent, hard-core pornography, but with children being given access to mobile devices, this is becoming increasingly difficult. It is no longer a question of: *if* your child comes across pornography, but *when*. Therefore, it is very important that both adults and children are educated in the potential impact of children being exposed to pornography, and what actions they need to take.

WHAT TO DO IF YOUR CHILD HAS SEEN PORNOGRAPHY

STAY CALM AND LISTEN: If your child confides in you, or you find out they have seen pornography, ensure your reaction is controlled and measured. It is important that you do not overreact and close down the conversation with your child. The way you communicate with your child will not only determine how comfortable they are in speaking with you about it further, but will also provide you with information about what it is they have actually seen.

Let them know you aren't angry with them (you may be disappointed), and reassure them that you are glad that you know, so you can help them make sense of what they saw. If you find yourself upset at any point in the conversation, reassure your child you aren't angry with them but simply upset at the situation. This will encourage your child to trust you and continue speaking with you.

GATHER INFORMATION: Ask them how they came to see these pictures or movies. Perhaps it was an accident or maybe they were curious and went searching for information. If someone else has shown them, let them know that it's okay for them to tell you who that person was, and if possible how old they were. Explain to your child it is against the law for anyone to show them private pictures or private movies. Discuss that the law says you need to be over 18 years of age to look at pictures or movies like these.

Determine if your child is regularly viewing pornography or if this was a one-off event. If they have developed a habit of frequently viewing pornography, you may like to consider seeking professional help.

REASSURE: Our children need to know they can come to us if they have any questions at all. They need to be reassured that they have done the right thing in telling you (or admitting they have seen pornography), and be encouraged to keep the lines of communication open for the future.

Try to steer clear of punishments such as removing devices, because this may cause embarrassment and confusion, particularly if your child has viewed the pornography by accident. You may need to create new rules about device usage. For example, mobile phones, tablets and computers are not allowed in bedrooms and there are set time frames in which these devices can be used. This is good practice to manage all forms of cyber safety.

You may want to speak with your child about your own experiences if you saw private pictures or movies as a child. As you speak, watch them for any indication they may need to continue to discuss and process what they have seen.

Children are naturally curious about bodies, sex, and the creation of babies. However, they do need to learn about it in a gradual and age-appropriate manner. Let them know that curiosity is okay, and encourage them to come and ask you questions about anything, at any time. There are many great resources available to help parents talk to their children about sex. For example *Talk Soon. Talk Often. – A Guide for Parents Talking to Their Kids About Sex.* (bit.ly/talk-soon-talk-often)

It is possible your child may use the internet to find out more about their bodies, sex, and the creation of babies, and find themselves viewing content that is upsetting and inappropriate. Encourage your child to come and tell you if they see any private pictures or private movies, or if someone ever tries to show them pornographic images.

DISCUSSION QUESTIONS

Below are some questions you can ask your child to see if they have comprehended the key concepts of this book:

Where could you see private pictures or private movies?

Why didn't Hayden-Reece tell his mum or another adult on his Safety Team straight away?

Can you think of any other reasons why Hayden-Reece may not tell his mum straight away that he has seen private pictures or private movies?

Who could you ask if you had a question about sex, bodies, or where babies come from?

Who is the first person you would tell if you saw a private movie or private picture?

Who are some other people you could tell?

Have you ever seen private pictures or private movies?

ADDITIONAL INFORMATION

Below is an introduction to some of the core concepts of the Safe4Kids Protective Education Program. It is important children have an understanding of these concepts to help keep them safe.

FEELINGS: When children are asked to name feelings or talk about their feelings, they find it difficult because they are not familiar with those words. Children need to understand that all feelings are okay; it's the negative behaviours that go with some feelings that are not acceptable. Everybody's feelings are different, and nobody can tell you how you should feel. Be mindful of saying to children, "Don't be scared," or, "Don't be silly," when they show signs of distress or discomfort about something. Instead, brainstorm with children what they can do to make themselves feel safer if they are feeling a negative emotion.

EARLY WARNING SIGNS: Early Warning Signs are our body's way of telling us that we feel unsafe. They are our "fight, flight, or freeze" response. They are also known as our intuition or "gut feelings". Early Warning Signs can be different for each of us, and include sweaty palms, feeling unable to move, rapid heartbeat, butterflies in our tummy, goose bumps, hair on our arms standing up, etc.

SAFETY TEAM OR NETWORK: A Safety Team is five trusted adults a child can talk with if they feel unsafe. Children need to know that these trusted adults will:

- listen to them

- believe them

- be available to them and

- take action if necessary, to help them feel safe again.

Help your child develop a Safety Team who will provide support and help protect them.

PERSISTENCE: When children need help, they must be taught to persist, to keep on asking for help until they receive it. If a child needs help, the first person they approach will not always listen to them or be able to help them. Children need to persist and keep telling trusted adults on their Safety Team, until their Early Warning Signs go away and they feel safe again. Persistence is of particular value in an emergency – when you need help immediately.

NAMES OF PRIVATE BODY PARTS: It is essential children are taught the correct anatomical names for their private body parts. Their private body parts are those parts covered by their bathers, and also their mouth. This is not sex education. It is merely teaching children the correct terminology, so that if they are subjected to abuse they can disclose the abuse using the correct private body part names, which has proven very beneficial in assisting prosecutors. It is also a deterrent for perpetrators if a child is able to use the correct names for their private body parts, since it is an indication that the child may have received some form of Protective Education.

SAYING "NO": Children are taught to respect their elders, to be polite and always to obey adults. Unfortunately, this can, and does, place them in harm's way. Children are often abused by people they know and trust. Children need to be taught that if they feel unsafe or have their Early Warning Signs it is okay to say "No" to anyone, especially if someone tries to touch their private body parts. It is also okay to break the rules of politeness and expected behaviour. If there is an emergency, then it's okay to interrupt adults, to keep themselves safe or help someone else in danger.

SECRETS: Children need to know that there are two kinds of secrets:

"Good" or "Safe" secrets are only kept for a short time, and will make someone happy when the secret is revealed. For example, a surprise birthday party, where everyone but the birthday person knows about the party for days or weeks in advance.

"Bad" or "Unsafe" secrets will make a child feel anxious, concerned or uncomfortable; they may have their Early Warning Signs. They will be told they must never tell, and that the secret must be kept for a long time, maybe even a lifetime. Unsafe secrets are kept by threats, coercion, bribes, and manipulation. Other ways children can identify a Bad or Unsafe secret is that there may only be two people who know the secret. Children need to know they should never keep Bad or Unsafe secrets, and always to tell someone on their Safety Team. Teach children they should never keep a secret about any kind of touching, even if they like the touch or the secret little special game.

For more information on child protection education and resources visit **www.safe4kids.com.au**

RECEIVING A DISCLOSURE:

If your child discloses that they have been abused, either physically, sexually or emotionally, here are some suggestions which may help your child, and you, to feel safe:

STAY CALM: Try to put your feelings aside, as an outraged reaction will only reinforce your child's reluctance to disclose. To help you stay calm and in control, try and remember the following three things you need to tell your child:

"I'm glad you told me"

"I believe you"

"It is not your fault".

BELIEVE YOUR CHILD: Children rarely lie about abuse, but they are often discouraged from disclosing because they think no one will believe them. It is therefore very important they know that you believe them.

OFFER REASSURANCE: Reassure your child that it is not their fault and they haven't done anything wrong; they are not to blame. You can also use phrases such as:

"You've done the right thing by telling me," or,

"I'm sorry this has happened to you and we'll work this out together."

DO NOT QUESTION YOUR CHILD: Do not pressure your child to give in-depth details. They may have to repeat their story for authorities and they may find it distressing each time they have to recount the abuse.

Do not approach the alleged perpetrator, leave this to the authorities.

MAKE NO PROMISES: Do not promise to keep this a secret. You may have to tell the authorities about what has happened.

CONTACT AUTHORITIES:
The Department for Child Protection

Police Child Protection Unit

OTHER CONTACTS: Kids Helpline 1800 55 1800 (Australia only) or www.kidshelpline.com.au